GROLIER

Your partner in education

**Distributed by Grolier, Sherman Turnpike
Danbury, Connecticut 06816**

©1991, 1984 The Child's World, Inc.
All rights reserved. Printed in U.S.A.

Grolier offers a varied selection of
children's book racks and tote bags.
For details on ordering, please write:
Grolier Direct Marketing
Sherman Turnpike
Danbury, CT 06816
Att: Premium Department

of this hole?"

asked
the hen,

the hog,

and the horse.

Down they went.

"How can we get out...

  hummingbird

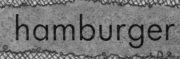 hamburger

 hammer

hood

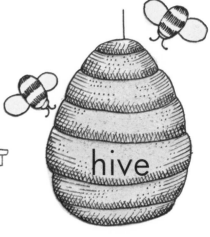 hive

 hospital

heart

29

More words with Little h.

hair

hotdog

harp

hand

honey

with all his things.

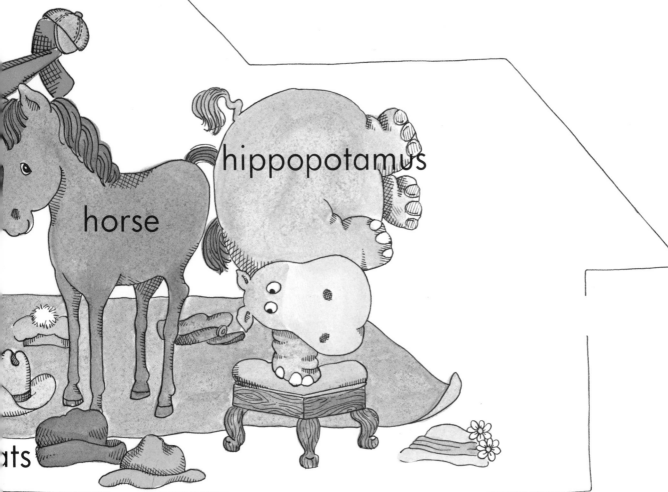

horse

hippopotamus

ats

Little h was happy ...

helicopter

hen

horn

hog

all the way home.